555
Sticker Fun
Christmas

IMAGINE THAT™

Licensed exclusively to Imagine That Publishing Ltd
Tide Mill Way, Woodbridge, Suffolk, IP12 1AP, UK
www.imaginethat.com
Copyright © 2021 Imagine That Group Ltd
EU Authorised Representative, The Merrion Buildings – Iconic Offices,
18-20 Merrion Street, Dublin 2, D02 XH98, Ireland
All rights reserved
2 4 6 8 9 7 5 3 1
Manufactured in China

Winter wonderland

Santa lives at the North Pole with his elves. Complete the winter wonderland scene with festive decorations and his busy little helpers.

THE
NORTH
POLE

A letter to Santa ...

Every year, Santa receives millions of letters from girls and boys around the world. Can you match the stamps on the letters to the stamps on the compartments to help Santa?

Santa's toyshop

Santa checks each letter that he receives from a child to make sure they get the right gift! Can you help him finish off this selection of perfect presents?

Let it snow, let it snow, let it snow ...

Santa's elves have got a day off and they're having lots of fun in the snow! Add more happy elves to the wintry scene.

Hide and snow seek!

Santa's reindeer are magical creatures, but they're also a bit naughty!
Can you find the hiding reindeer, and place them in the stables,
so they can eat and rest before Christmas Eve?

Turning on the lights

Tonight, the Christmas lights will be turned on in the city centre. The mayor presses a switch and the streets are filled with sparkling lights. Add some more Christmas shoppers.

Carol service

The local church is holding a carol service. The congregation is really getting into the holiday spirit, as they sing songs that are filled with festive good cheer. Add the choir to the scene.

Neighbourhood fun

Everyone in the neighbourhood has been busy decorating their homes for Christmas. Can you help them finish the job?

Deck the halls

This home is being prepared for Christmas.
Deck the halls with pretty Christmas
cards and festive displays.

At the ice rink

An ice rink has opened in the city centre for the Christmas holiday season. Add smiling children to the rink, as they skate along to Christmas music.

At the toyshop

The toyshop is very busy as children look at the toys they hope to get for Christmas. Fill the shelves with lots of toys for good girls and boys.

Do you want to build a snowman?

It has been snowing, and the children are busy building snowmen, making snow angels and sledging down the hill. Complete the fun winter scene.

Christmas shopping

Far away from the North Pole, people are getting ready for Christmas. Complete this happy festive scene as people buy gifts for their friends and family.

School nativity

It is the day of the school play and the children are acting out the nativity. Finish the scene so they can get started!

Party time

A party to celebrate Christmas is in full swing and everyone is dancing and having fun! Add some more balloons and people to the merry scene.

Elves' workshop

The elves are busy making lots of toys for good girls and boys.
Complete this busy workshop scene.

Santa's sleigh

It is Christmas Eve and Santa is getting ready for his busiest night of the year! Help him load the sleigh with lots of presents for good boys and girls.

Christmas Eve

It is Christmas Eve and children all over the world are hoping they will receive a visit from Santa. Hang out stockings, and add some food and drink for Santa and his reindeer.

Up, up and away!

The presents are loaded onto the sleigh and it's time for Santa to go! He must visit every boy and girl on this special night. Add more of Santa's reindeer team to the starry night sky.

Express delivery!

Santa stops his reindeer on a snowy rooftop to deliver presents to the children who are fast asleep in bed. Add him climbing down the chimney, and add presents and stockings in the living room.

On Christmas Day in the morning

It's early on Christmas morning and children are playing with new toys that have been delivered by Santa! Complete the scene.

Christmas lunch

It is time to eat and the whole family is spending time together. Complete the happy table scene with *yummy festive food!*

The real meaning of Christmas

Christmas is a time to spend with friends and family. At this special time of year, we celebrate the birth of a very special baby, Jesus. Complete the nativity scene.

Advent Calendar

Complete this countdown to Christmas by finding the sticker for each day.

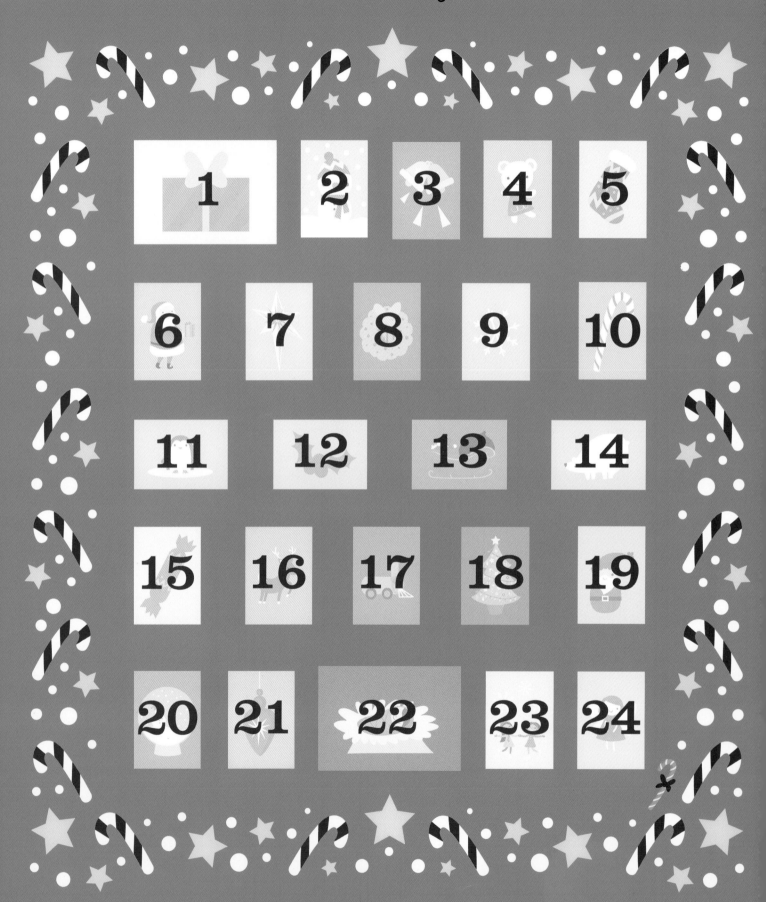